Show 3.

I will draw 3 🍎.

Strengthen: *What can you use to help you show 3? Is there another way to show 3? How do you know you've got 3?* [Reinforce touching objects or pictures as the child counts.] *What could you draw to show 3?*
Deepen: *How many different ways can you find to show 3? Look at a partner's work. What's the same? What's different? Talk to your partner about other ways you could show 3.*

3

How many are there?

How many  can you see?

ELG 11: Mathematics: Numbers count reliably with numbers from 1 to 4
ELG 2: Communication and language: Understanding answer 'how' and 'why' questions about their experiences and in response to stories or events

Strengthen: *Can you use a five frame to help you count? Can you touch each object as you count? Does it matter that one of the cars is red? How many are there altogether?*
Deepen: *Can you find another way to show four cars on a five frame? Where else could you put the cars? Do you need to count each object? Can you see how many, without counting?*

4

Show 4.

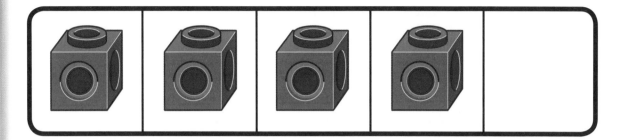

I can make 4 in lots of ways.

 Strengthen: Encourage children to place cubes on the five frame in the same places as the picture. *Can you move one cube at a time to show 4 in a different way? How many spaces are there on the five frame? Are there always the same number of spaces when you use 4 cubes in a five frame? How do you know?*
Deepen: *How many different ways can you find to show 4? Look at a partner's work. What is the same? What is different?*

How many 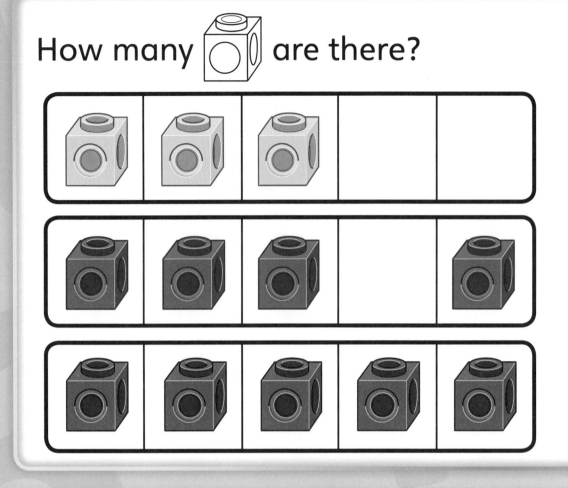 are there?

Can you see 5?

  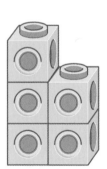

ELG 11: Mathematics: Numbers count reliably with numbers from 1 to 5

 Strengthen: *Can you touch each cube as you count? How many spaces are there? Can you make the pictures with cubes?*

Deepen: *Can you make 5 a different way? Show me with cubes. Does it matter what colour the cubes are? Do you always need to count to know that there are 5 here? How can you see 5?*

6

Draw a 5 party!

 Ask

Strengthen: *What can you draw at the party? Can you draw 5 of each? Can you touch each object to count?*
Deepen: *How many different ways can you show 5? What can you draw at the party? Can you think of 5 different ways to show 5? What has your partner drawn? What is the same? What is different?*

Circle each group.

Spot the **odd one out**.

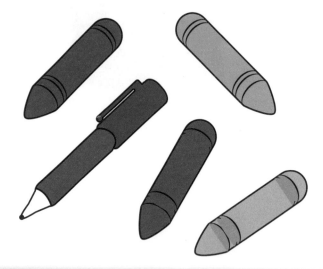

ELG 11: Mathematics: Numbers children count reliably with numbers from 1 to 20
ELG 12: Mathematics: Shape, space and measures explore characteristics of everyday objects

Strengthen: *Describe what you see in the pictures. Can you spot the difference? Which are the same? When you sort them into two groups, what will you put together? What does 'odd one out' mean? Does it matter if the crayons are different colours? Which one does not belong?*
Deepen: *Is there more than one way to sort what you see? Is there a way to sort into more than two groups? Describe how you have sorted what you see to your partner.*

Sort some toys into 2 groups.

> I can sort my toys in more than I way.

Strengthen: *What can you find in the classroom to sort? How could you sort your collection into two groups? [Ask children to physically place the items in the boxes.] How did you decide to sort your collection? By colour? Shape? Size?*

Deepen: *Describe to your partner how you have sorted your collection. Is there more than one way to sort your collection? How do you know? Is it possible to sort your collection into three groups or even four? How many different groups can you make with your collection?*

Who has more ?

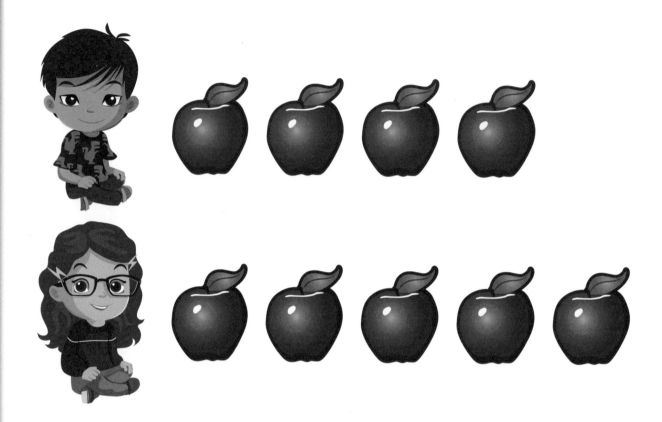

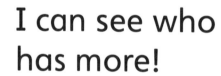

I can see who has more!

ELG 11: Mathematics: Numbers count reliably with numbers from 1 to 5, say which number is one more or one less than a given number

 Strengthen: *Can you use cubes to help you compare? Who has more apples? Can you circle the child with more apples?*

Deepen: *Who has more apples? Who has fewer apples? Is fewer the same or different from more? How do you know?*

Show a ladybird with more spots.

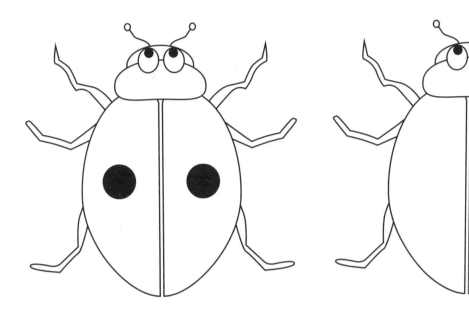

I think there is more than one way.

Ask **Strengthen:** *How many spots does this ladybird have? Can you make it with cubes? Do you need more or fewer cubes? How can you make more?*
Deepen: *If this ladybird has 2 spots, how many could be more? Is there more than one answer? Have you got the same answer as your partner?*

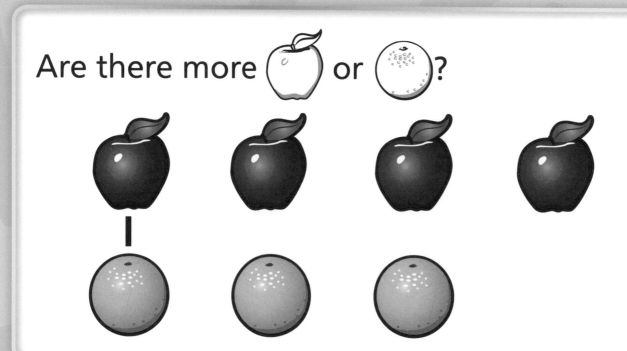

ELG 11: Mathematics: Numbers count reliably with numbers from 1 to 5, say which number is one more or one less than a given number

 Strengthen: *Can you use cubes to help you? Where could you put the cubes?* [One cube on each picture.] *How can you move the cubes to help you? Can you match them up?*
Deepen: Make an obvious mistake by matching two objects to one. Ask children to explain where you have gone wrong.

Draw more than .

First I will count the .

Strengthen: *How many oranges are there? Can you use yellow cubes to represent them? What does 'more' mean? Let's get some red cubes – can you lay out more red cubes than yellow cubes? How many red cubes do you have? Can you draw that number of apples?*
Deepen: Make an obvious mistake by using 2 cubes to represent the apples (fewer, not more) or 4 cubes to represent the oranges. Ask children to explain where you have gone wrong.

Draw the 'now' picture.

First

Then

Now

Show one more than 3.

ELG 11: Mathematics: Numbers count reliably with numbers from 1 to 5, and say which number is one more than a given number.

Ask **Strengthen:** *Let's tell the story. 'First there is one caterpillar ... then ...' Would using cubes help? How many cubes do you need to start the story? How many cubes do you need to add?*
Deepen: *Can you work out 'one more' in your head? What is one more than 4? What is one more than 1? First you have 2 cubes, now you have 3 cubes. How many cubes were added?*

Draw a story about one more.
First

Then

Now

I will start with 2.

Strengthen: *What can you use to help you draw a story about one more? Can you use the five frame and cubes to show me? What number will you start with? Then what will you do? So 'now' you have ...? Can you draw this story?*
Deepen: *Can you make up a story to describe one more than 4? Can you make up a different story? Listen to your partner's one more stories. Check them together.*

15

Draw the 'now' picture.

First

Then

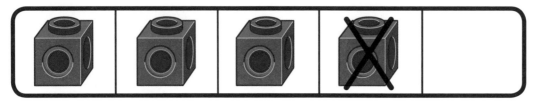

Now

Show one less than 5.

ELG 11: Mathematics: Numbers count reliably with numbers from 1 to 5, and say which number is one less than a given number

Strengthen: *Let's act out the story. First there are 4 cubes. How many cubes are there to start with? How many cubes have been crossed out? How many cubes are there now? Use cubes to show me the story. Can you use 'first', 'then' and 'now'?*

Deepen: *Can you work out one less in your head? What is one less than 5? What is one less than 2? First I have 4 cubes, now I have 3 cubes. How many cubes were taken away? How could you show one less than 1? What would the 'now' look like?*

Draw a story about one less.

First

Then

Now

I will cross one out to show one less.

 Ask **Strengthen:** *Can you show one less than 5 using different objects? Can you use the five frame and cubes? Show me. How do you know you have made one less?* (Reinforce touching objects or pictures as the child counts.) *How can you make this into a story about one less? How will you show one less? What could the story be about? Can you draw it for me?*
Deepen: *Can you make up a different story about one less? Listen to a partner's story about one less. How was their story different to your story? How was their story the same? How did they show one less?*

What does Isha do after school?

ELG 3: Communication and language: Speaking
develop their own narratives and explanations by connecting ideas or events

ELG 12: Mathematics: Shape, space and measures
use everyday language to talk about time
recognise, create and describe patterns

ELG 13: Understanding the world: People and communities
talk about past and present events in their own lives and in the lives of family members

 Ask

Strengthen: *Look at the first picture. Where is Isha? What is she doing? Is it day or night? How do you know? What does she do next? Look at the sky. What time of day is it? What happens later? Who is picking her up from Grandma's house? Where might they be going? What do you think will happen next? Tell a first, then, later story about these pictures.*

Deepen: *What is happening in each picture? Are they in the right order? How do you know? What time do you think it is in each picture? Which one do you think happens at 4 o'clock? Could Isha go to the park when her dad collects her? Why or why not? [It would be too dark.] What do you think will happen next? How do you know?*

What do you do each day?

What do you do first?

 Ask

Strengthen: *How can you show me what happens in your day? Could you draw or take photos? What was the first thing you did today? Was it light or dark outside? Was it day or night? What did you do next? Did you do anything else before you came to school? What did you do after you got to school?*

Deepen: *What was the first thing you did today? What time of day was it? [Morning, afternoon, evening.] How do you know? [It was light outside.] What did you do before you came to school? And before that? Why do you do that in the morning? Could you do that at the end of the day instead? Why? What will you do after lunch or after school today?*

Number practice

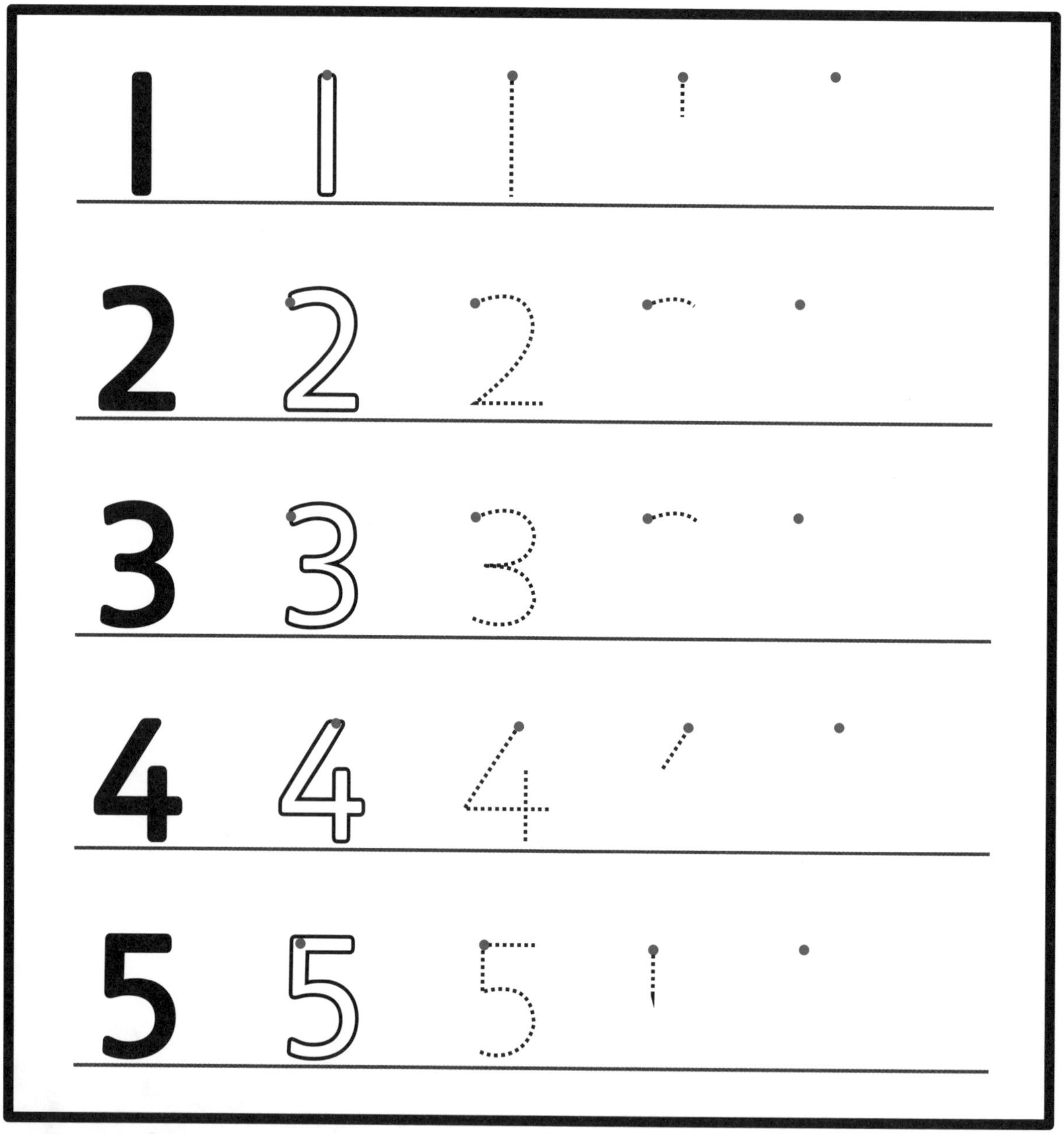

1 1 1 1 1

2 2 2 2 2

3 3 3 3 3

4 4 4 4 4

5 5 5 5 5

Use this page however you want.

Use this page however you want.

Use this page
however you want.

Reception
Maths Journal **A**

How to use this book

We recommend that children have adult support to use this book. Children who struggle with mark-making can demonstrate their mathematical understanding by placing real-life objects, such as cubes, on the page.

Practice pages encourage children to practise the new skills they have learned in their Power Maths lessons.

Reflect gives children an opportunity to demonstrate their depth of understanding at the end of each week.

At the bottom of each page you will find prompt questions for the adult helper:

Strengthen questions support children who are not sure where to start.

Deepen questions encourage children to develop a deeper understanding of the concept.

Ash

Astrid

Sparks

Published by Pearson Education Limited, 80 Strand, London, WC2R 0RL.
www.pearsonschools.co.uk

Text and design © Pearson Education Limited 2019
Edited by Pearson and Just Content Ltd
Design templates created by Kamae Design
Typeset by PDQ Media
Original illustrations © Pearson Education Limited 2019
Illustrated by Andrew Painter and Nadene Naude at Beehive Illustration

Cover design by Pearson Education Ltd
Cover illustration by Andrew Painter
Back cover illustration by Andrew Painter

Power Maths Series Editor and Power Maths Reception Consultant: Tony Staneff

Written by White Rose Maths (Beth Smith, Amy How, Jane Brown and Faye Hirst), Beth Smith, Katie Williams, Faye Hirst and Caroline Hamilton.

First published 2019

23 22 21 20 19

10 9 8 7 6 5 4 3 2 1

British Library Cataloguing in Publication Data
A catalogue record for this book is available from the British Library
ISBN 978 1 292 28607 5

Note from the publisher
Pearson has robust editorial processes, including answer and fact checks, to ensure the accuracy of the content in this publication, and every effort is made to ensure this publication is free of errors. We are, however, only human, and occasionally errors do occur. Pearson is not liable for any misunderstandings that arise as a result of errors in this publication, but it is our priority to ensure that the content is accurate. If you spot an error, please do contact us at resourcescorrections@pearson.com so we can make sure it is corrected.

www.pearsonschools.co.uk
myorders@pearson.com

ISBN 978-1-292-28607-5

Pearson